KT-473-289

This I-Spy book belongs to:

_____

Afghanistan
The horizontal tricolour of black, red, and green with the state coat of arms was officially established in 1980.
I-Spy for 10

Albania
It was in 1912, after independence from the Turks, that Albania revived its fifteenth-century red flag with the double-headed black eagle.
I-Spy for 5

Algeria
White for purity, green for the Moslem world; the star and crescent are also associated with Islam.
I-Spy for 5

American Samoa
Eastern Samoa has had connections with the United States since the late nineteenth century and its flag includes the American eagle as well as its own staff and club, symbols of rule.
I-Spy for 10

Andorra
The tricolour of Andorra in the Pyrenees includes the colours of France and Spain who have guaranteed the independence of the state since the thirteenth century.
I-Spy for 5

Angola
Industry, farming, black Africa, and freedom are symbolized by the half gear wheel, the machete, the black stripe, and the red stripe.
*I-Spy for **5***

Antigua and Barbuda
Part of the Leeward Islands, these island states achieved independence from Britain in 1981 but the flag design goes back to the late 1960s. The black in the flag symbolizes the origins of the population in Africa.
*I-Spy for **10***

Argentina
Dating from the early nineteenth century, the colours recall the blue and white cockade worn by members of the Liberation Army.
*I-Spy for **5***

Australia
This is basically a British Blue Ensign with the star beneath the Union Flag representing the Australian states and the other stars depicting the Southern Cross constellation.
*I-Spy for **5***

Austria
Although it has a much earlier origin, the present red and white striped flag of Austria dates from the end of World War 2.
*I-Spy for **5***

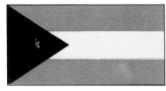

Bahamas
The Bahamas became independent from Britain in 1973 when the current flag was first flown. The colours are for sea, land, and unity.
I-Spy for 5

Bahrain
The division between the red and white band may either be a straight line or saw-edged. The red symbolizes a particular Moslem sect.
I-Spy for 5

Bangladesh
Bangladesh separated from Pakistan in 1971. The flag is a Moslem green field for farming with a blood-red disc representing the struggle for freedom.
I-Spy for 5

Barbados
In this Caribbean island, the blue and the gold symbolize sea and sand, while the trident reflects its colonial days.
I-Spy for 5

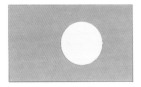

Belau
The yellow disc is for the full moon, a symbol of human work, peace, and love while the blue of the flag stands for the independence of this Pacific island.
I-Spy for 15

Belgium

Belgium achieved its independence in 1830, but the black, yellow, and red tricolour are the colours of the duchy of Brabant dating from the eighteenth century.

I-Spy for 5

Belize

The coat of arms in the white central disc symbolizes the trade from which this former British colony earns most of its foreign revenue — timber. The red stripes were added in 1981 to represent the Union Democratic Party.

I-Spy for 5

Benin

The green field of the flag is for farming while the red star stands for communism. This flag came into being in the mid-1970s. Benin is a small state in West Africa between Togo and Nigeria.

I-Spy for 10

Bermuda

The flag of Bermuda is a British Red Ensign with the Crown Colony's own state arms. The Red Ensign is the United Kingdom's civil ensign and may reflect the fact that merchant ships were the first to come ashore here.

I-Spy for 5

Bhutan
Bhutan is a small kingdom in the Himalayas. The colours of its flag stand for royal power and the Buddhist religion while the dragon represents authority and benevolence.

I-Spy for 15

Bolivia
Courage, mineral wealth, and farming are symbolized by the red, yellow, and green in the flag of this South American country which achieved its independence in the late nineteenth century.

I-Spy for 5

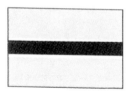

Botswana
Black and white people living together under a common blue sky are represented by the black and white stripes on a blue background for this southern African nation's flag.

I-Spy for 5

Brazil
Forests and gold are symbolized by the green and the yellow, while the stars on the globe represent the states and territories of this vast South American country.

I-Spy for 5

British Virgin Islands

This is a British colony as it has been since the seventeenth century. Its flag is a Blue Ensign with the country's state arms of a virgin with the twelve oil lamps of the Biblical parable.
I-Spy for **5**

Brunei

The independent state of Brunei is situated in northern Borneo and maintains close connections with Britain, as it has since the late nineteenth century. The crescent in its flag symbolizes Islam.
I-Spy for **5**

Bulgaria

Peace, the fruitfulness of the land, and valour are symbolized by the white, green, and red stripes of Bulgaria's tricolour which was designed in the late nineteenth century.
I-Spy for **5**

Burma (Myanmar)

Today's flag stems from the early 1970s when the cogwheel and the vital rice crop to indicate industry and farming were added to the blue of the night sky on a red field of courage.
I-Spy for **5**

Burundi
This central African nation adopted its flag on independence in 1962. The stars are for 'Unity, Work, and Progress' while the colours are for the fallen, for hope, and for peace.
I-Spy for 10

Cameroon
The central red band serves to unite the green hope of the south of the country and the yellow sun of the north, with the star representing Cameroon administration.
I-Spy for 5

Canada
Since 1965, Canada has flown the red and white flag with the emblem of the maple leaf. Red and white are the country's national colours.
I-Spy for 5

Cape Verde
This archipelago off the west coast of Africa was a Portuguese colony until 1975. The red stands for blood, the green for hope, and the yellow for the sun.
I-Spy for 15

Cayman Islands
The flag is the British blue ensign with the country's coat of arms which shows, among other things, a turtle that recalls the name Christopher Columbus first gave these islands — the Tortugas.
I-Spy for 10

Central African Republic
Red blood, green hope, and yellow sun are common to African flags which, in this case, also includes the colours of the French tricolour. The star is for liberty.
I-Spy for 10

Chad
Chad is a land-locked, former French colony in Equatorial Africa. Its tricolour, flown since the late 1950s, has blue for the sky, yellow for the sun, but the red in Chad's flag represents forward-looking nationhood.
I-Spy for 10

Chile
Red stands for the blood of Chile's fallen heroes, blue is for the sky; the white symbolizes the snow on the Andes mountains. The star is for the state.
I-Spy for 5

Colombia
This is a tricolour that harks back to Colombia's Spanish past as symbolized by the red band. Its place in the American continent is indicated by the yellow while the blue stands for the Atlantic Ocean.
I-Spy for 5

Comoro Islands

This republic is a group of islands in the Mozambique Channel to the north-west of Madagascar. The green and the crescent are for the Moslem religion while the stars represent the four main islands.

I-Spy for **15**

Congo

This Equatorial African state achieved full independence from France in 1960. Here red is for Communism, with common African colours of green and yellow. The palm fronds stand for peace.

I-Spy for **5**

Cook Islands

These islands, named after Captain Cook, are situated in the South Pacific. The 15 stars on a blue field symbolize the islands while the Union Flag shows the connections with the British Commonwealth.

I-Spy for **25**

Costa Rica

This Central American republic's flag harks back to the federation it had in the early nineteenth century with the other provinces of the Central American Union. It now bears the state arms of Costa Rica.

I-Spy for **5**

Cuba

The red is for blood and freedom, the blue and white stripes for the provinces from which modern Cuba is composed, and the single star stands for independence.

I-Spy for 5

Cyprus

Although Greek and Turkish flags are mainly to be seen on the island, the nation's flag shows a yellow map (for its copper deposits) with olive branches for peace between the two states of Greece and Turkey.

I-Spy for 5

Czechoslovakia

The unusual arrangement of the commonly used red, white, and blue stand for the colours of Bohemia and Slovakia.

I-Spy for 5

Denmark

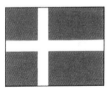

Some authorities suggest that the Danish flag, officially adopted in the mid-nineteenth century, may have its origins as early as the thirteenth century making it one of Europe's oldest.

I-Spy for 5

Djibouti

This former French colony on the
north-east African coast achieved
independence in 1977. The white
triangle symbolizes peace and
equality with its red star for unity.
The blue stands for the sea and
the sky while the green is for
the land and Islam.
I-Spy for 10

Dominica

The dark green background is for
plant life while the three colours in
the cross are for the black African
population, the white waterfalls
and rivers, and the yellow for the
Indian members of the population.
The red disc is for socialism while
the stars are for the states;
the parrot is the national bird.
I-Spy for 10

Dominican Republic

Red and blue symbolize blood and
freedom while the white cross
symbolizes this Hispaniolan
republic's religion.
I-Spy for 10

Ecuador

Red is for the blood of the fallen.
The yellow is for sun and for the
country's natural riches while the
blue symbolizes sea and
sky.
I-Spy for 5

Egypt

The black in this tricolour is a reminder of Egypt's many years of oppression. The red is for blood and the white is for a bright and peaceful future. The state arms is a golden falcon.

I-Spy for 5

El Salvador

This central American republic is situated on the isthmus connecting North America with South America. The two blue stripes symbolize the waters on either side — the Pacific and the Caribbean Sea.

I-Spy for 5

Equatorial Guinea

This state lies on the coast of West Africa to the south of Cameroon. The blue triangle is for the sea while the red, white, and green are for blood, peace, and the land. The flag also bears the state arms.

I-Spy for 10

Ethiopia

The red, yellow, and green of the Ethiopian tricolour have been adopted widely throughout Africa. The colours here suggest blood, peace and natural riches, and the earth.

I-Spy for 5

Falkland Islands

The British Blue Ensign bears the colony's arms with a ram to symbolize the sheep which provide most of the islands' income and the ship of the English navigator, John Davis, who discovered the Falklands.

*I-Spy for **5***

Fiji

There are more than 800 islands in this former British colony of the south-west Pacific. The blue field bears the Union Flag and the state arms which includes a white dove of peace.

*I-Spy for **10***

Finland

Finland achieved its independence from Russia in 1917. The blue and white of its flag are for sky and snow.

*I-Spy for **5***

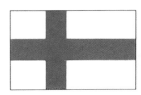

France

The red, white, and blue of the Tricolour may date back to the colours associated with the three saints St Denis, St Joan, and St Martin but it was first flown in 1794 during the French Revolution.

*I-Spy for **5***

14

Gabon

The flag of this West African
republic is a tricolour with green for
the land of forests, yellow for the
sun, and blue for the sea.
I-Spy for 10

Gambia

The central blue
stripe is for the
River Gambia
while, in this
case, red stands
for the sun and
green for
farming. The
white stripes
symbolize peace.
I-Spy for 5

Germany (Federal Republic)

The three colours of the Federal
Republic of Germany's flag are
those of the Republic founded at
Weimar in 1919, and are linked
with German aspirations for unity.
The post-war East and West
Germanys were unified into the
Federal Republic in
October 1990.
I-Spy for 5

Ghana

The former British colony of the
Gold Coast has used 'pan-African'
colours to represent blood, natural
resources, and farming while the
black star symbolizes the
freedom of Africa.
I-Spy for 5

Gibraltar

This British colony's state flag is the Union Flag but its civil flag is three towers on a white field to show the 'Rock's' key position at the mouth of the Mediterranean.
I-Spy for 5

Greece

Blue and white are the colours of Otto of Bavaria, King of Greece from 1833, as well as those used during the Greek wars of independence. The cross is for the Greek Orthodox religion.
I-Spy for 5

Grenada

The colours of this West Indian island's flag are for blood and courage (red), the sun (yellow), and farming (green). The seven stars are for the areas of the state while the nutmeg shows the importance of this plant to the economy.
I-Spy for 5

Guam

Guam is an United States military base in the western Pacific. Its territorial flag, bearing the state seal, usually flies alongside the Stars and Stripes.
I-Spy for 15

Guatemala

The two blue bands represent the Pacific Ocean and the Caribbean Sea to the west and east of this Central American State. The state arms are included.

Guinea

This West African republic has taken the 'pan-African' colours for its flag but arranged them in a vertical tricolour similar to that of the French.

I-Spy for 10

Guinea-Bissau

Formerly a Portuguese colony, the flag is that of the African Party for the Independence of Guinea and Cape Verde in the 'pan-African colours'. The black star symbolizes the Party.

I-Spy for 15

Guyana

This unusual flag was designed by an American and adopted in 1966. Green is for the plant life, yellow for mineral wealth, white for the rivers, and the building of the nation is represented by the red triangle edged with black.

I-Spy for 5

Haiti

The black and red bands of this Hispaniolan republic's flag represent the black (the majority) and mixed-race element's in the nation's population.

I-Spy for 10

Honduras

The flag of Honduras is similar to that of El Salvador and others who became independent as part of the Central American Federation. The five stars indicate the country's wish for the five states to join together again.
I-Spy for 5

Hong Kong

Until 1997, when the agreement between Britain and China is enacted, Hong Kong flies the British Blue Ensign bearing the state arms of this British crown colony.
I-Spy for 5

Hungary

The red, green, and white colours of the Hungarian flag have a long history but the tricolour, with its French influence, was first flown in the mid-eighteenth century.
I-Spy for 5

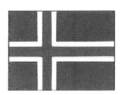

Iceland

This volcanic island republic has been independent from Denmark since 1941 but its flag continues to bear the traditional Scandinavian cross.
I-Spy for 5

India
India achieved its independence from Britain in 1947. Green is for faith, orange for courage, and white for peace. The blue of the ancient Indian *chakra* — which symbolizes renewal — is for sky and sea.
I-Spy for 5

Indonesia
Indonesia consists of many south-east Asian equatorial islands which were formerly the Dutch East Indies. The colours of the simple flag have a long history.
I-Spy for 5

Iran
Green is for Islam, white is for peace, and red is for courage. The five elements of the state arms represent the five religious obligations of Islam.
I-Spy for 5

Iraq
Iraq is the ancient country of Mesopotamia through which flow the Tigris and Euphrates rivers. Red is for blood and valour, white for peace, and black for Islam's victories. The green stars are for Islam and for the hope of union with Egypt and Syria.
I-Spy for 5

Ireland

Ireland has been a republic since 1949. The colours of its tricolour are green for Ireland and the Roman Catholic majority, orange for the Protestant minority, and white for peace between them.
I-Spy for 5

Israel

Israel has been a Jewish republic since its creation in 1948. The flag's design echoes the *tallith*, or prayer shawl while, at the centre, is the Star of David.
I-Spy for 5

Italy

Italy's tricolour was adopted officially after the end of World War 2 but it is based on the standard used by Napoleon I in his Italian campaign of the late eighteenth century.
I-Spy for 5

Ivory Coast (Côte d'Ivoire)

Formerly a French territory, the flag of this West African republic is similar in design to the Tricolour but has the colours orange for progress, green for the forests, and white for peace and unity.
I-Spy for 10

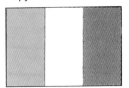

Jamaica

The yellow St Andrew's Cross separates the green triangles of farming and hope from the black ones representing the past and future problems.
I-Spy for 5

Japan

The red disc on a white field symbolizes the land of the rising sun. The sun is also, in legend, the ancestor of the Japanese emperor.
I-Spy for 5

Jordan

The black, white, green, and red colours of the Jordanian flag are those of other Arab states but the 7-pointed white star represents the first 7 verses of the Holy Book, the Koran.
I-Spy for 5

Kampuchea (Cambodia)

The turbulent history of this small south-east Asian country has meant a succession of flags since 1945. But successive governments have all chosen red as the dominant colour with a symbol of the great temple of Ankor Wat.
I-Spy for 5

Kenya
Red and black are for blood and for the black population, while green is for this East African country's natural resources. The white stripes are for peace and the shield and spears are for the continuation of freedom.
I-Spy for 5

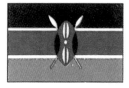

Kiribati
Kiribati is an independent state consisting of a number of widely scattered islands in the Pacific. Its flag represents the sun rising over the Pacific with a Frigate Bird above.
I-Spy for 15

Korean Democratic People's Republic
North Korea adopted its flag in 1948. White is for purity, blue for the hope of peace in the future, and the red and the red star are for the Communist state.
I-Spy for 5

Kuwait
The flag of this tiny Arab state, independent from Britain since 1961, has green for the earth, white for achievement, red for blood, and black for the battles that have been fought.
I-Spy for 5

Laos
The flag of the People's Democratic Republic of Laos in southeast Asia is effectively that of the Pathet Lao communist movement which eventually ousted the monarchy in 1975.
I-Spy for 5

Lebanon
The recent history of Lebanon has been one of prolonged civil war, but its national flag stands for sacrifice and for peace, while the emblem on the white field is a Cedar of Lebanon.
I-Spy for 5

Lesotho
The hat symbol represents the Basotho people of this southern African state. White is for peace and the blue field for the sky, while the red and green stripes are for faith and the earth.
I-Spy for 5

Liberia
This state in West Africa was founded in 1847 by free slaves from the USA. The 11 stripes are for the men who signed the bill of independence. The blue field is for Africa and the star is for the independent nation.
I-Spy for 5

For an extra point, why not colour in each country as you Spy its flag?

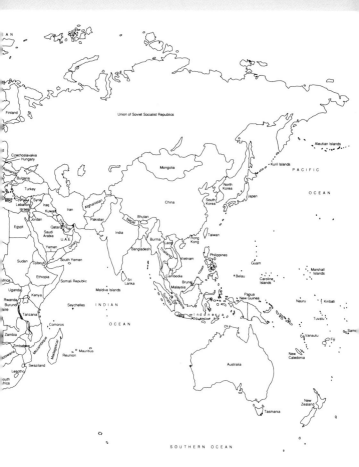

Some very small islands or countries do not appear on this map. When you Spy the flag of one of these countries, double the score.

Libya
Green is the symbol of Islam but, in the case of this North African republic, it also symbolizes the so-called 'Green Revolution' proclaimed by Colonel Qaddafi to feed its people.
I-Spy for 5

Liechtenstein
The principality is situated between Switzerland and Austria. The colours of its flag symbolize the sky (blue) and the fire of the hearth and home (red) while the gold crown is for government and unity.
I-Spy for 10

Luxembourg
The red, white, and blue tricolour of Luxembourg's flag is intended to reflect the country's belief in the principles which inspired the French Revolution.
I-Spy for 5

Madagascar
The republic consists of the large island off the East coast of Africa. The red and white colours represent the immigrant south-east Asian population while the green is for Indian Ocean people.
I-Spy for 10

Malawi

Black is for the African people, red for the blood lost in the fight for independence, and green for the earth. The rising sun symbolizes the dawing of a new age.
I-Spy for 5

Malaysia

The red and white colours are traditional in south-east Asia. The blue symbolizes the connexion with the British Commonwealth and the yellow is a royal sultanate colour.
I-Spy for 5

Maldives

The red and the green symbolize blood and peace, while the white crescent represents Islam. The Maldives are a chain of coral islands in the Indian Ocean.
I-Spy for 10

Mali

The red, yellow, and green tricolour of this West African republic recall its former status as a French colony in Africa. These colours were also those of the movement which led to independence.
I-Spy for 10

Malta

Red and white were the colours of Count Roger, the eleventh-century Norman invader of the island. The white field bears a British George Cross awarded to the island for its valour during World War 2.
I-Spy for 5

Marshall Islands

The blue field of this flag stands for the Pacific Ocean where the islands are located. White is for brightness, orange for courage, and the position of the star shows the nearness to the Equator.
I-Spy for 25

Mauritania

This Islamic state in West Africa has adopted a flag in which the colours and the symbols are typically Moslem and African.
I-Spy for 10

Mauritius

The colours of the four-banded flag are for blood (red), the sea (blue), freedom (yellow), and the earth (green). Mauritius, in the Indian Ocean, gained independence from Britain in 1968.
I-Spy for 10

Mexico

The tricolour of green, white, and red symbolizes freedom, faith, and unity while the state arms have Aztec origins.
I-Spy for 5

Micronesia
The four stars, probably derived from those of the United States flag, represent the four member states. The blue field represents the Pacific Ocean.
I-Spy for 25

Monaco
The colours of the simple flag of this tiny principality on the Mediterranean coast are believed to have their origins in the fourteenth century.
I-Spy for 5

Mongolia
Red is for Communism, blue is for the sky, and yellow is the colour symbolizing brotherhood of the nation. The star of Communism sits upon various ancient Mongolian symbols.
I-Spy for 10

Montserrat
The flag of this British colony in the Caribbean is a Blue Ensign bearing the state arms of a woman holding a cross and a harp.
I-Spy for 10

Morocco
Red has been used as the colour for the Moroccan flag for at least 300 years. The green star-shaped design in the centre is the pentangle known as the 'Seal of Solomon'.
I-Spy for 5

Moçambique

This was a former Portuguese colony in East Africa. Its complex flag symbolizes shed blood, farming, resources, workers, farmers, and thinkers, as well as independence and the defence of nationhood.

I-Spy for 10

Nauru

This is a small, former Australian trust island in the Pacific just to the south of the Equator. Its flag represents its geographical position as well as the 12 tribes on the island.

I-Spy for 25

Nepal

The sun and the moon featuring on Nepal's uniquely shaped flag portray the idea that the nation should be as long lasting as these two heavenly bodies.

I-Spy for 10

Netherlands Antilles

These Dutch Caribbean islands which have been self-governing since 1954 contain the colours of the Netherlands flag with 6 stars to represent the islands.

I-Spy for 25

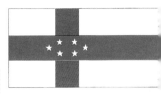

Netherlands

Originally, the Dutch tricolour was orange, white, and blue but, in 1937, the colour of the House of Orange was changed to red.

I-Spy for 5

New Zealand
New Zealand's flag is a British Blue Ensign with four stars to represent the heavenly constellation of stars known as the Southern Cross.
I-Spy for 5

Nicaragua
The Nicaraguan flag represents the country's location in the Central American isthmus: a white band lying between the two blue bands of the Pacific Ocean and the Caribbean Sea.
I-Spy for 5

Niger
The tricolour of this West African republic includes an orange band for its deserts, white for purity, and a green band for the fertile land of the south. The orange disc represents the sun.
I-Spy for 10

Nigeria
The simple two-colour design of the Nigerian flag was adopted in 1960 when the country became independent. Green is for farming and the white is for peace.
I-Spy for 5

Northern Marianas
The blue field of this flag represents the Pacific Ocean while the white star is for the Commonwealth of Northern Marianas. The grey stone design beneath the star is a symbol from the ancient culture of the islands.
I-Spy for **25**

Norway
The Danish flag is a white cross on a red field: this represents Norway's dominance by Denmark for almost 500 years. During the time when Norway and Sweden were united in the nineteenth century, a blue cross was laid on the white.
I-Spy for **5**

Oman
The sultanate's flag has red for the Kharÿite Moslems, who comprise most of the population, green for Islam, and white for peace and purity. The flag also includes the state arms.
I-Spy for **5**

Pakistan
The green field with its white crescent and star are for the Moslem state while the narrower white band symbolizes the minority religious faiths.
I-Spy for **5**

Panama

The red and the blue quarters are for the country's traditional Liberal and Conservative Parties. The white stands for agreement between them while the stars are for loyalty and the law.

I-Spy for 5

Papua New Guinea

The flag shows the union of the two states of Papua and New Guinea which took place in 1975. The stars are the Southern Cross and there is a golden bird of paradise.

I-Spy for 10

Paraguay

The conventional red, white, and blue horizontal tricolour is made unusual by having the state arms on the obverse and the seal of the treasury on the reverse of the flag.

I-Spy for 5

People's Democratic Republic of Yemen (South Yemen)

This flag includes the traditional Arab red, white, and black tricolour but with a blue triangle to symbolize the people and a red star for the National Liberation Front.

I-Spy for 10

People's Republic of China

Red is generally thought to be the colour of Communism but it is also a traditional colour in Chinese flags. The larger star is for Communism, however, while the four smaller ones are for farmers, manual labourers, office workers, and managers.

*I-Spy for **5***

Peru

The red and white are said to represent the colours of a flamingo and were selected by General José de San Martín during the wars against Spain in the early part of the nineteenth century.

*I-Spy for **5***

Philippines

Blue and red are for nobility and courage: the white triangle stands for freedom. The three stars are the the country's main areas while the 8-rayed sun suggests the first 8 areas to rebel against Spain.

*I-Spy for **5***

Poland

This simple red and white flag bears the colours which have always been associated with Poland throughout its long and troubled history.

*I-Spy for **5***

Portugal

The red and green colours are linked with the overthrow of the monarchy in 1910. The state arms are placed on a navigational instrument which symbolizes Portugal's maritime empire.
I-Spy for 5

Puerto Rico

The Puerto Rican flag was adopted in 1895 and has a similar design to that of Cuba except that the blue and the red have been reversed.
I-Spy for 5

Qatar

Qatar gained its independence from Britain in 1971. Originally, the flag was red and white but the dye turned brown in the sunlight so that, eventually, the brown colour was adopted.
I-Spy for 5

Republic of China (Taiwan)

Red is for the blood of the people, white is for honesty and brotherhood, and blue is for justice. The sun was the symbol for the Kuomintang Party.
I-Spy for 5

Republic of Korea
The white field is for peace and purity: the central design is the ancient mystical symbol of yin and yang. The four black designs are for the four seasons and the four cardinal compass points.
I-Spy for 5

Romania
The blue, yellow, and red tricolour is thought to derive from the ancient flags of Transylvania, Moldavia, and Walachia. The flag also bears the state arms.
I-Spy for 5

Rwanda
The red, yellow, and green colours are those of many African states and here represent blood, peace, and hope for the future. The R is for Rwanda.
I-Spy for 10

Sahara
The Sahraoui Arab Democratic Republic is recognized by many African countries but its existence is still in dispute. Its flag has the usual Arab colours with the crescent and star for Islam.
I-Spy for 15

St Christopher and Nevis

The two stars on the central black diagonal stand for the two states of St Christopher and Nevis. In 1976, Anguilla was separated from St Christopher and Nevis to be a British Dependency.

I-Spy for **20**

St Helena

St Helena is a British Crown Colony in the Central Atlantic. Its flag is a Blue Ensign with the state badge showing a sailing ship approaching safe anchorage.

I-Spy for **10**

St Lucia

The island triangle is on a field of blue representing the sea. Black is for the volcanoes from which the island is composed while yellow is for the golden sand of its beaches.

I-Spy for **10**

St Vincent and the Grenadines

Green is for the fertile earth, yellow for the sun, and blue for sky and sea. An earlier flag had white stripes either side of the yellow as well as the state arms — now stylized.

I-Spy for **10**

San Marino
This is an ancient and independent
republic in the Italian Apennines.
The blue and the white are
symbolic of sky and snow.
*I-Spy for **10***

Saudi Arabia
The green field of the Saudi flag
represents Islam while the inscrip-
tion above the sword of authority
reads: 'There is no god but
Allah; Muhammad is the
Prophet of Allah'.
*I-Spy for **5***

São Tomé and Príncipe
This former Portuguese colony off
the coast of West Africa uses the
colours which many African nations
have chosen for their flags. The two
stars designate the two islands from
which the state is composed.
*I-Spy for **20***

Senegal
Once again the green, yellow, and
red are those of the pan-African
ideal while the green star is a
symbol of African freedom.
*I-Spy for **10***

Seychelles
This group of islands in the Indian
Ocean achieved independence from
Britain in 1976. The green is for
farming, the red for revolution, while
the wavy band between symbolizes
the riches of the sea.
*I-Spy for **10***

Sierra Leone
The flag of this coastal West African republic has green for hills and for farming, white for peace and justice, and blue for the Atlantic Ocean.
I-Spy for 5

Singapore
In this flag, red is for brother-hood, white is for purity, the cresent moon is for the birth of a nation, and the stars stand for equality, justice, democracy, peace, and progress.
I-Spy for 5

Solomon Islands
The blue, yellow, and green represent the Ocean, the sun, and the land. The stars indicate the islands from which the country is composed.
I-Spy for 15

Somalia
The blue field reflects the colour of the flag of the United Nations which helped the country to independence in 1960. The white star suggests freedom and its points indicate the 5 regions which make up the country.
I-Spy for 10

South Africa

The colours of the South African flag are those of the House of Orange and were used by the early Dutch settlers. The three flags in the central design represent the regions of the country.

I-Spy for **5**

Spain

Red and gold have been the Spanish colours for more than 200 years but the actual form of the civil flag dates from 1936 and the state flag from 1981.

I-Spy for **5**

Sri Lanka

Ceylon, as it was then called, gained independence in 1948 and became the Democratic Socialist Republic in 1978. The green and orange stripes are for Hindus and Moslems while the lion with sword is a sixth-century device.

I-Spy for **5**

Sudan

Red is for blood and the socialist revolution, white for peace, green for Islam and prosperity, and black is for the fact that the word *sudan* means 'black' in Arabic.

I-Spy tor **10**

Suriname
Suriname, in South America, was a Dutch colony until 1975. The colours here mean love (red), justice (white), fields and forests (green), while the yellow star symbolizes the progress of the nation.
I-Spy for 10

Swaziland
In the flag of this southern African kingdom, blue means peace, yellow mineral riches, and crimson the blood shed in the past. The arms consist of Zulu spears, a shield, and royal decorative plumes.
I-Spy for 10

Sweden
The blue and gold colours of Sweden's flag are thought to derive from the country's coat of arms which dates back some 600 years.
I-Spy for 5

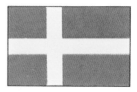

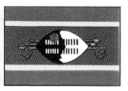

Switzerland
The holy white cross on a red field may date back to the thirteenth century or even earlier.
I-Spy for 5

Syria
Syria Adopted the red, white, and black tricolour flag with its two green stars in 1980.
I-Spy for 5

41

Tanzania

Tanzania includes Zanzibar and Pemba. The green is for Tanganyika, the blue for Zanzibar, and the yellow stripes for mineral wealth. The black diagonal is for the largest element in the population.
I-Spy for **5**

Thailand

The red, white, and blue of this four-banded flag represent blood and sacrifice, purity, and the royal family.
I-Spy for **5**

Togo

Each colour here represents more than one thing. Red is for blood and love, green for hope and the earth's resources, yellow for work and mineral wealth, and the white star for wisdom and hope.
I-Spy for **15**

Tonga

The red cross on a white field is for the Christian population of these Friendly Islands in the Pacific Ocean.
I-Spy for **10**

Trinidad and Tobago

Red is for the sun and for generosity, white is for the sea and equality, and black is for determination and unity.
I-Spy for **5**

Tunisia

The flag of Tunisia — similar to that of Turkey — has the red field, star, and crescent which were the symbols of the Ottoman Empire of which it was once a part.

I-Spy for 5

Turkey

This flag has its origins in the Ottoman Empire which controlled large areas of Africa, Asia, and Europe for more than 600 years from the beginning of the fourteenth century.

I-Spy for 5

Turks and Caicos Islands

The flag of these two groups of islands in the Caribbean Sea is a British Blue Ensign bearing the state arms.

I-Spy for 15

Tuvalu

The Union Flag on a pale blue field indicate the connection with Britain. Each of the stars represents one of these Pacific islands, eight of which are inhabited.

I-Spy for 20

Uganda

The flag of this East African republic is striped with black for the African population, yellow to symbolize the sun, and red for unity. The flag also bears an emblem of a crested crane.

I-Spy for 5

Union of Soviet Socialist Republics

Red has long been the colour of revolution and is often used to represent Communism. The 5-pointed star symbolizes the unity of five continents while the hammer and sickle represent workers and peasants.

I-Spy for 5

United Arab Emirates

Green and black are the colours of Arab unity while red and white have long been included among the colours of the 7 sheikhdoms which make up the United Arab Emirates.

I-Spy for 5

United Kingdom of Great Britain and Northern Ireland

The Flag of the Union includes the cross of St George for England, that of St Andrew for Scotland, and St Patrick for Ireland. Strictly, it should be called the Union Jack only when flown at the 'jack' or bow of a ship.

I-Spy for 5

United States of America

The flag is often known as the 'Stars and Stripes' or the 'Star-Spangled Banner'. The 13 stripes symbolize the original 13 states of the Union, while the 50 stars represent the states which make up the modern United States.

I-Spy for 5

United States Virgin Islands
Formerly the Dutch West Indies, the islands became an American dependency in 1917. The American eagle is on a white field with the letters V and I for Virgin Islands.
I-Spy for 25

Upper Volta (Burkina Faso)
This West African state is named after its location on the upper reaches of the River Volta. The colours of the flag come from local names of the main branches of the river: 'white', 'red', and 'black'.
I-Spy for 15

Uruguay
The colours reflect Uruguay's earlier connection with Argentina while the 9 stripes represent the regions into which the country was divided. The sun symbolizes freedom and independence.
I-Spy for 5

Vanuatu
The black triangle is for the earth and the people. The red is for blood; the green is for the islands. The yellow Y-shape is for the enlightenment of Christianity and echoes the arrangement of the islands in the Pacific.
I-Spy for 25

45

Vatican City State
White and yellow have been the colours of the Papacy since the early part of the nineteenth century. The white half of the field also has the Vatican coat of arms.
I-Spy for 10

Venezuela
The yellow stands for the American continent, the blue for the Atlantic Ocean, and the red for Spain. The 7 stars represent the original provinces of which the country was composed.
I-Spy for 5

Vietnam
The red field — long associated with socialism and Communism — is for blood and revolution while the 5-pointed star is for workers, peasants, young people, soldiers, and the intelligentsia.
I-Spy for 10

Western Samoa
Red, white, and blue here symbolize blood and courage, freedom and independence, and purity. The stars are for the constellation of the Southern Cross.
I-Spy for 15

Yemen Arab Republic
The red is for revolution, the white for faith and purity, and the black represents the country's history. The green star is for Islam and independence.
I-Spy for 10

Yugoslavia
Red, white, and blue have long been the colours of the Slavic peoples while the red star represents Communism.
I-Spy for 5

Zaire
The red, yellow, and green are the colours adopted by many independent African states. The black arm holding a flaming torch is taken from the symbol of the People's Revolutionary Movement.
I-Spy for 10

Zambia
The green field is for farming, the black for the people, red for blood spilled in the fight for freedom, and orange for the mineral riches of the country. The eagle symbolizes Zambia's future.
I-Spy for 5

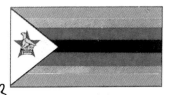

Zimbabwe
Black is for the black African peoples, red for blood, yellow for mineral resources, green for farming, and white for peace. The red star is for socialism and overprinted on it is an ancient bird symbol.
I-Spy for 5

INDEX

© I-Spy Limited 1991

ISBN (paperback) 1 85671 009 2
ISBN (hard cover) 1 85671 010 6

Michelin Tyre Public Limited Company
Davy House, Lyon Road, Harrow, Middlesex HA1 2DQ

MICHELIN and the Michelin Man are Registered Trademarks of Michelin

All rights reserved. No part of this publication may be reproduced, stored in a retrieval system, or transmitted in any form or by any means, electronic, mechanical photocopying or otherwise without the prior written permission of I-Spy Limited.

A CIP record for this title is available from the British Library.

Edited and designed by Curtis Garratt Limited, The Old Vicarage, Horton cum Studley, Oxford OX9 1BT

Flag artwork reproduced by permission of Michelin. Additional flag artwork by Taurus Graphics. Title page photograph: Hutchison Library.

Colour reproduction by Norwich Litho Services Limited.

Printed in Spain.